gets you through

CW00572177

AQA GCSE 9-1

DESIGN AND TECHNOLOGY

PRACTICE TEST PAPERS

PAUL ANDERSON
DAVID HILLS-TAYLOR

Contents

ACKNOWLEDGEMENTS

The author and publisher are grateful to the copyright holders for permission to use quoted materials and images.

All images are © Shutterstock.com

Every effort has been made to trace copyright holders and obtain their permission for the use of copyright material. The author and publisher will gladly receive information enabling them to rectify any error or omission in subsequent editions. All facts are correct at time of going to press.

Published by Letts Educational
An imprint of HarperCollins*Publishers*
1 London Bridge Street
London SE1 9GF

ISBN: 9780008321758

First published 2019

10 9 8 7 6 5 4 3 2

© HarperCollins*Publishers* Limited 2019

Commissioning Editor: Kerry Ferguson
Authors: Paul Anderson and David Hills-Taylor
Project Management: Katie Galloway and Chantal Addy
Editorial: Jill Laidlaw
Cover Design: Amparo Barrera
Inside Concept Design: Ian Wrigley
Text Design and Layout: Jouve India Private Limited
Production: Karen Nulty
Printed and bound by CPI Group (UK) Ltd, Croydon, CR0 4YY

GCSE
Design and Technology

Time allowed: 2 hours

Materials

For this paper you must have:

- normal writing and drawing instruments
- a calculator
- a protractor.

Instructions

- Use black ink or black ball-point pen. Only use pencil for drawing.
- Answer **all** questions.
- Answer the questions in the spaces provided. Do not write on blank pages.
- Do all your rough work in this book and cross through any work that you do not want to be marked.

Information

- The marks for questions are shown in brackets.
- The maximum mark for this paper is 100.
- There are 20 marks for Section A, 30 marks for Section B and 50 marks for Section C.

SECTION A – Core Technical Principles

Questions **1–10** are multiple choice questions. For each of these questions you should shade in **one** lozenge. If you make a mistake, cross through the incorrect answer and shade the correct response.

1   Which one of the following sources of energy is a fossil fuel?

    A   Biomass   ◯

    B   Nuclear   ◯

    C   Oil   ◯

    D   Solar   ◯

[1 mark]

2   An engineer is designing a system to warn chefs when the temperature in their fridge is getting too high. What is the output in this system?

    A   Buzzer   ◯

    B   Microcontroller   ◯

    C   Switch   ◯

    D   Temperature sensor   ◯

[1 mark]

3   Which one of the following best describes a finite resource?

    A   It will always cost less than a non-finite resource   ◯

    B   It will always cost more than a non-finite resource   ◯

    C   It will eventually run out   ◯

    D   It will never run out   ◯

[1 mark]

4   Which one of the following is an alloy?

     A   Brass   ○

     B   Copper   ○

     C   Tin   ○

     D   Zinc   ○

[1 mark]

5   Which of the following is a social movement that helps producers in developing countries get better prices for their products?

     A   Co-operative   ○

     B   Crowd funding   ○

     C   Fair trade   ○

     D   Virtual marketing   ○

[1 mark]

6   Which of the following is a renewable energy source?

     A   Coal   ○

     B   Gas   ○

     C   Oil   ○

     D   Wind   ○

[1 mark]

7 Which type of paper is commonly used for leaflets, as it resists inks and colours seeping through it?

A   Bleed-proof paper ⬭

B   Cartridge paper ⬭

C   Grid paper ⬭

D   Layout paper ⬭

[1 mark]

8 Which one of the following polymers can be reshaped when it is heated?

A   Epoxy resin ⬭

B   Melamine formaldehyde ⬭

C   Polyester resin ⬭

D   Polypropylene ⬭

[1 mark]

9 What type of lever is shown in **Figure 1**?

Figure 1

A   First order ⬭

B   Second order ⬭

C   Third order ⬭

D   Fourth order ⬭

[1 mark]

| 1 | 0 | What does the term 'fusibility' describe?

    A   The ability of a material to burn   ⬭

    B   The ability of a material to melt when heated   ⬭

    C   The ability of a material to provide electrical resistance   ⬭

    D   The ability of a material to be stretched without breaking   ⬭

[1 mark]

| 1 | 1 |.| 1 | **Figure 2** shows a simple gear train.

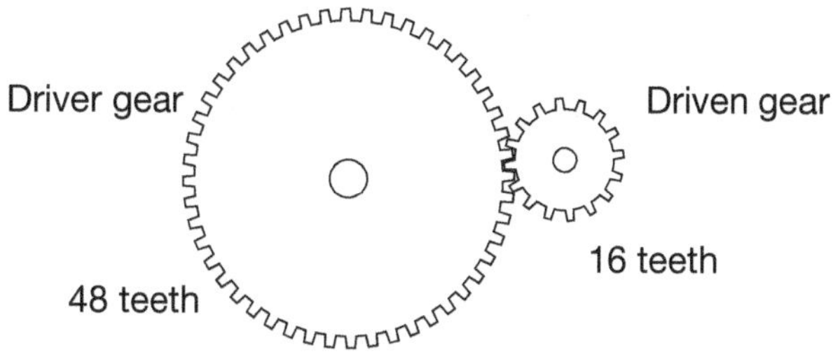

Driver gear   Driven gear

48 teeth   16 teeth

Figure 2

Calculate the gear ratio of this gear train.

[2 marks]

11.2 Name a mechanical linkage that can be used to change the direction of linear motion by 90°.

[1 mark]

....

12.1 'Modern materials' is a class of materials that have been developed through the invention of new or improved processes. Name a 'modern material'.

[1 mark]

....

12.2 State **two** properties of the modern material you have named in question **12.1**.

[2 marks]

....

....

....

13 Give **one** advantage and **one** disadvantage of using solar power to generate power.

[2 marks]

Advantage ....

....

....

Disadvantage ....

....

Figure 3 shows a design for a hand-held games system.

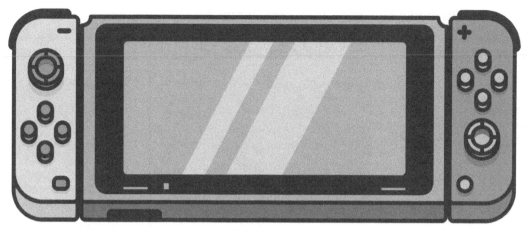

Figure 3

State **two** features that could be included in the design to allow for maintenance.

[2 marks]

1 ....

....

....

2 ....

....

....

SECTION B – Specialist Technical Principles

Choose **one** product or component from **Figure 4**.

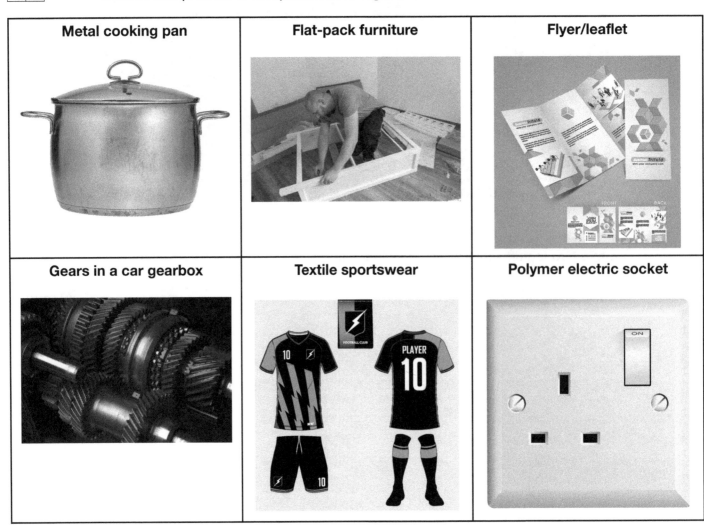

| Metal cooking pan | Flat-pack furniture | Flyer/leaflet |
| Gears in a car gearbox | Textile sportswear | Polymer electric socket |

Figure 4

Name of product/component: ....

`15`·`1` Name a specific material used to make the product/component.

[1 mark]

....

`15`·`2` Explain **two** reasons why the material used is suitable for use in this product/component.

[4 marks]

Reason 1 ....

....

....

....

Reason 2 ....

....

....

....

| 1 | 5 | · | 3 | Using notes **and/or** sketches, describe briefly how the product/component you have chosen would be manufactured.

[4 marks]

| 1 6 | Describe the typical characteristics of the following types of production.

| 1 6 · 1 | Prototype production

[2 marks]

....

....

....

....

| 1 6 · 2 | Batch production

[2 marks]

....

....

....

....

....

| 1 6 · 3 | Mass production

[2 marks]

_____

_____

_____

_____

_____

_____

| 1 7 | Choose **one** of the products listed in **Table 1**.

A monthly magazine	The wheel for a child's toy, made from wood	A block of metal with a milled slot	A template made from laser-cut polymer	Curtains with a printed repeating design	A printed circuit board (PCB)

Table 1

Name of product/component: _____

| 1 7 · 1 | Describe a quality control system that may be used during the manufacture of your chosen product.

[3 marks]

_____

_____

_____

_____

_____

_____

| 1 | 7 | · | 2 | The part you have chosen has one feature with a dimension of 45 mm and a tolerance of 2 mm. Calculate the acceptable maximum and minimum sizes of the feature.

[2 marks]

....

....

....

....

....

| 1 | 8 | When designing and manufacturing products, designers often consider ecological issues. These may include, for example, product mileage, carbon production and deforestation.

Evaluate the importance of considering ecological issues when designing and manufacturing products.

[10 marks]

....

....

....

....

....

....

....

SECTION C – Designing and Making Principles

Figure 5 shows a mobile phone designed to help elderly people communicate with friends and family members.

Figure 5

Specification:

- Lightweight and portable
- Simple function – text messages and phone calls only
- Large buttons
- Battery powered

1 9   Study the mobile phone and the information shown above.

19.1 Choose **two** of the specification points given.

For each, explain why it was included.

[4 marks]

Specification point 1: ....

Explanation ....

....

....

....

....

Specification point 2: ....

Explanation ....

....

....

....

....

19·2 Explain **one** improvement that would make the phone more suitable for the target audience.

[3 marks]

19·3 Explain how the design of the phone would need to be modified if the target audience was changed to teenagers.

[4 marks]

....

....

....

....

....

2 0 The mobile phone shown on page 18 is powered by a battery. The company collected data on how long the batteries lasted before they needed replacing, see **Table 2**. Data was recorded for 50 products.

No battery needed replacing in less than 50 hours. All of the batteries needed replacing in less than 150 hours.

Battery life, hours	50 < 70	70 < 90	90 < 110	110 < 130	130 < 150
Cumulative total number of failed batteries	1	5	14	30	50

Table 2

2 0·**1** Produce a line graph of the cumulative battery life.

[5 marks]

20.2 Calculate the mean average number of hours for the life of the batteries.

[2 marks]

20.3 Determine the time at which 50% of the batteries needed to be replaced.

[2 marks]

20 . 4   Explain the difference between the values calculated in **20.2** and **20.3**.

[2 marks]

2 1   The mobile phone shown on page 18 was designed using a systems approach.

2 1 . 1   Explain **two** advantages of using a systems approach when designing.

[4 marks]

2 1 · 2   An iterative process was also used when designing the phone. Describe what is meant by an iterative design process.

[4 marks]

2 1 · 3   Name **two** design strategies other than the systems approach and iterative design process.

[2 marks]

Explain what is meant by 'design fixation'.

[3 marks]

`2` `2`   **Figure 6** shows a shape that is to be marked out for cutting.

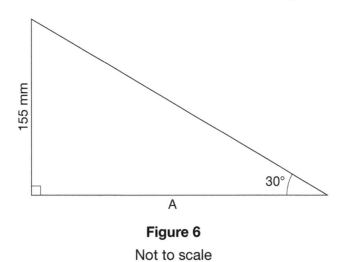

Figure 6

Not to scale

2 2 . 1 Calculate the length of side A. Give your answer to **one** decimal place.

[2 marks]

2 2 . 2 Explain the purpose of datums when marking out materials.

[2 marks]

2 2 . 3 Give **two** methods of reducing waste when cutting or shaping materials.

[2 marks]

1

2 ....

2 | 3 · 1   Give **two** reasons why surface treatments or finishes are applied to materials.

[2 marks]

1 ....

2 ....

2 | 3 · 2   Name **two** examples of surface treatments or finishes.

[2 marks]

1 ....

2 ....

23·**3** For one of your answers given in question **23.2**, use notes and sketches to describe how this surface treatment or finish would be applied to a material.

[5 marks]

END OF QUESTIONS

GCSE
Design and Technology

Time allowed: 2 hours

Materials

For this paper you must have:

- normal writing and drawing instruments
- a calculator
- a protractor.

Instructions

- Use black ink or black ball-point pen. Only use pencil for drawing.
- Answer **all** questions.
- Answer the questions in the spaces provided. Do not write on blank pages.
- Do all your rough work in this book and cross through any work that you do not want to be marked.

Information

- The marks for questions are shown in brackets.
- The maximum mark for this paper is 100.
- There are 20 marks for Section A, 30 marks for Section B and 50 marks for Section C.

SECTION A – Core Technical Principles

Questions **1–10** are multiple choice questions. For each of these questions you should shade in **one** lozenge. If you make a mistake, cross through the incorrect answer and shade the correct response.

1   Which one of the following is a ferrous metal?

    A   Aluminium   ◯

    B   Brass   ◯

    C   Tin   ◯

    D   Tool steel   ◯

[1 mark]

2   A designer is developing a system to automatically open a door when someone stands on a pressure sensor. What type of component is a pressure sensor?

    A   Input   ◯

    B   Process   ◯

    C   Programmable   ◯

    D   Output   ◯

[1 mark]

3   Which one of the following involves burning a fuel to generate electricity?

    A   Biomass   ◯

    B   Hydro-electric   ◯

    C   Tidal   ◯

    D   Wind   ◯

[1 mark]

4 A new product includes a removable cover so that the batteries can be replaced when they run out. This is an example of:

A   anthropometric design ☐

B   design for maintenance ☐

C   flexible manufacturing ☐

D   planned obsolescence ☐

[1 mark]

5 Which one of the following best describes market pull?

A   Advertising to increase the number of customers for a product ☐

B   Prices for products being reduced over time ☐

C   Products produced due to new technologies becoming available ☐

D   The development of new products due to consumer demand ☐

[1 mark]

6 What type of motion is shown in **Figure 1**?

Figure 1

A   Linear ☐

B   Oscillating ☐

C   Rotary ☐

D   Reciprocating ☐

[1 mark]

7 Which term means the ability of a material to return to its normal shape after being stretched or squeezed?

    A   Absorbency

    B   Elasticity

    C   Hardness

    D   Malleability

[1 mark]

8 Which one of the following is a softwood?

    A   Balsa

    B   Mahogany

    C   Oak

    D   Pine

[1 mark]

9 Which one of the following is a synthetic material?

    A   Cotton

    B   Larch

    C   Nylon

    D   Wool

[1 mark]

1 0   Which one of the following describes duplex board?

A   It is only made from bleached wood pulp, with no
     recycled content   ○

B   Usually brown in colour, this low-cost board has a top
     and bottom layer between which there is a layer that is
     fluted or triangulated to add rigidity   ○

C   It has white surfaces with grey fibres between   ○

D   It has a layer of aluminium foil on one side   ○

[1 mark]

1 1 · 1   Describe briefly how electricity is generated using nuclear power.

[2 marks]

1 1 · 2   Name **two** types of system used to store energy after it is generated.

[2 marks]

1 2 · 1   Name a smart material.

[1 mark]

....

1 2 · 2   For the material you have named in **12.1**, state the property that makes it a smart material.

[1 mark]

....

....

....

1 3   **Figure 2** shows a fork made from stainless steel.

Figure 2

State **two** reasons why forks are often made from stainless steel.

[2 marks]

1 ....

....

2 ....

....

| 1 | 4 |

A first class lever is being used to raise a load of 90 N. See **Figure 3**. The effort to move the load is 30 N.

Calculate the mechanical advantage.

90 N   30 N

Fulcrum

Figure 3

[2 marks]

SECTION B – Specialist Technical Principles

1 5 Choose one product or component from **Figure 4**.

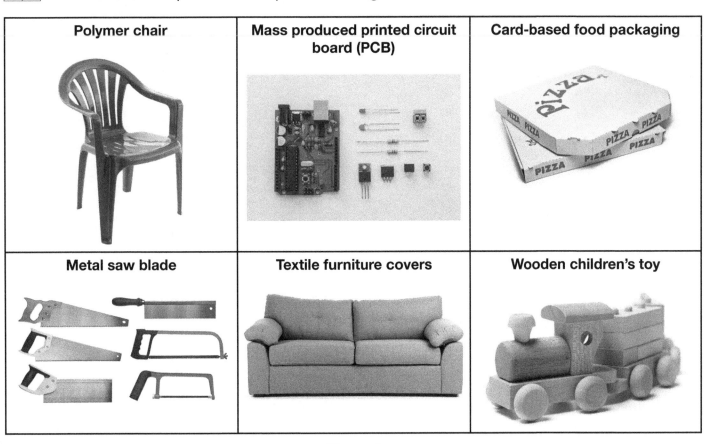

| Polymer chair | Mass produced printed circuit board (PCB) | Card-based food packaging |
| Metal saw blade | Textile furniture covers | Wooden children's toy |

Figure 4

Name of product/component: ....

1 5 · 1   Explain how the material could be modified to improve **one** property or characteristic of this product.

[4 marks]

For the product you have chosen, explain how **two** of the 6 Rs can be used to make the products more sustainable.

[4 marks]

1 ....

....

....

....

....

2 ....

....

....

....

....

1 6 Choose a material from the following list:

- Cartridge paper
- Spruce moulding
- Zinc sheet
- Polyvinyl chloride rod
- Elastane fabric

Selected material: ....

Describe how the material you have selected is converted from raw material to a usable form.

[4 marks]

Choose one of the commercial products in **Figure 5**.

Pop-up book	Metal cylinder block	Polymer toy
Wood baseball bat	**Circuits in a mobile phone**	**Curtains**

Figure 5

Name of product/component: ....

1 7 · 1   Describe briefly the commercial manufacturing processes used to make your chosen product.

[4 marks]

....

....

....

....

....

....

| 1 7 · 2 | When selecting the materials or components to make your chosen product, several different factors are considered. These typically include, for example, the mechanical properties and social factors.

Other than mechanical properties and social factors, explain **two** other factors that would typically be considered.

[4 marks]

1 8 Companies often consider social issues when designing and manufacturing products. These may include, for example, working conditions, pollution and the impact of the product and it's manufacture on others.

Evaluate how the consideration of social issues may affect the design and manufacture of products.

[10 marks]

....

....

....

....

....

....

....

....

....

....

....

....

....

....

SECTION C – Designing and Making Principles

Figure 6 shows a range of chairs made from different materials.

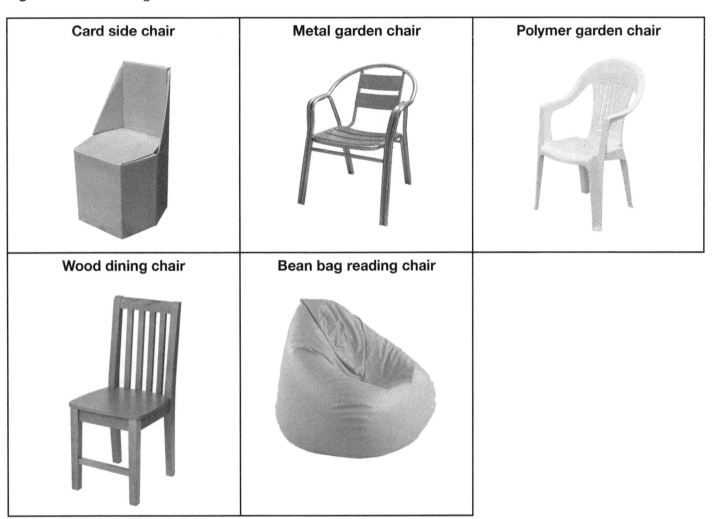

| Card side chair | Metal garden chair | Polymer garden chair |
| Wood dining chair | Bean bag reading chair | |

Figure 6

1 9   Choose **one** of the chairs shown in **Figure 6**.

     Name of chair: ....

19 · 1   Evaluate the ergonomics of your chosen chair.

[4 marks]

19 · 2   Your chosen chair is to be redesigned in the style of a past or present designer.

Name **two** past or present designers.

[2 marks]

1 ....

2 ....

1 9 . 3   Using notes and sketches, redesign your chosen chair in the style of **one** of the designers named in question **19.2**.

[6 marks]

| 2 | 0 | | User-centred design was applied during the design of the chairs shown in **Figure 6**.

| 2 | 0 |·| 1 | | Explain **two** advantages of user-centred design as a design strategy.

[4 marks]

1 ....

....

....

....

....

2 ....

....

....

....

....

2 0 · 2   State **two** disadvantages of user-centred design as a design strategy.

[2 marks]

1 ....

....

....

2 ....

....

....

2 0 · 3   Another example of a design strategy is the systems approach.

Explain what is meant by the systems approach.

[2 marks]

....

....

....

....

....

2 1 **Figure 7** shows a shape that is to be cut for a chair.

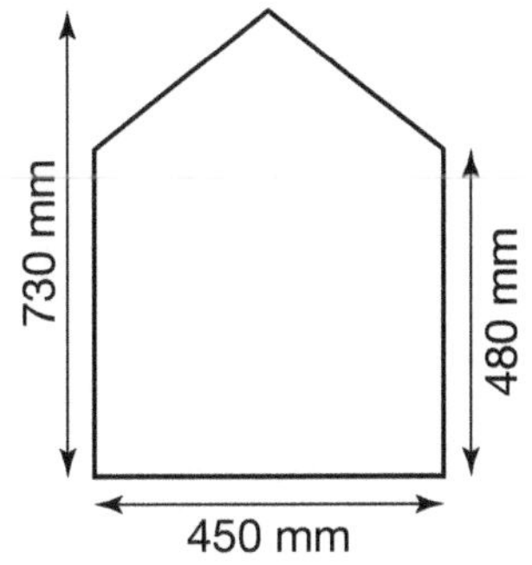

Figure 7

Not to scale

2 1 · 1 Calculate the area of the shape.

[4 marks]

2 1 . 2   It was decided to reduce the area of the shape by 15%.

Calculate the new area of the shape. Give your answer in standard form.

[3 marks]

2 1 . 3   The width of the shape is to be cut to 450 mm. The tolerance of this value is +/- 2 mm.

Calculate the maximum and minimum permissible width of the shape.

[2 marks]

| 2 | 2 | Using an example, explain how jigs can be used to ensure accuracy when producing prototypes.

[6 marks]

23.1 The times taken to produce 10 prototypes of a product were measured in seconds:

880, 872, 898, 820, 845, 810, 880, 885, 876, 855.

Calculate the mean average time to assemble **one** prototype.

[2 marks]

23.2 The cost of labour is £15 per hour. Calculate the labour cost to produce one mean average prototype. Give your answer to **two** decimal places.

[2 marks]

2 3 · 3 Explain why designers produce prototypes of products or systems.

[3 marks]

_____

_____

_____

_____

_____

_____

2 4 · 1 Describe what is meant by the term 'design specification'.

[2 marks]

_____

_____

_____

_____

_____

| 2 4 | · | 2 | Describe **three** items of information that should be included in a manufacturing specification.

[6 marks]

1 ....

....

....

....

....

2 ....

....

....

....

....

3 ....

....

....

....

....

END OF QUESTIONS

PRACTICE EXAM 1

SECTION A – Core Technical Principles

1.	C	**[1]**
2.	A	**[1]**
3.	C	**[1]**
4.	A	**[1]**
5.	C	**[1]**
6.	D	**[1]**
7.	A	**[1]**
8.	D	**[1]**
9.	B	**[1]**
10.	B	**[1]**

11.1 Gear ratio = number of teeth on driven gear: number of teeth on driver gear
Gear ratio = 16:48 **[1]**
Reducing to lowest common denominator
Gear ratio = 1:3 **[1]**
Note: this must be presented as a ratio. Marks will not be awarded for a decimal value, i.e. 0.33.

11.2 Bell crank **[1]**

12.1 1 mark for naming a modern material, such as: graphene, metal foams, titanium, coated metals, liquid crystal displays, nanomaterial.

12.2 1 mark each for stating two relevant properties of the material given in 12.1, e.g. high strength, low density, high rigidity, resistance to creep, resistance to corrosion, etc.

13. 1 mark for an advantage, such as: sustainable, low operating cost once installed, etc.
1 mark for a disadvantage, such as: only works when there is sunshine, energy needs to be stored for use at other times, not able to react to short-term changes in demand, etc.

14. 1 mark each for two suitable reasons, such as:
- Access panels for repairs.
- Replaceable batteries/rechargeable.
- Use of materials that can be wiped clean.
- Ports to allow for software updates/ game modifications.
- Use of standard parts or modular parts, to allow for repair.
- Any other appropriate answer.

SECTION B – Specialist Technical Principles

15.1 1 mark for naming an appropriate material, for example:
- Metal cooking pan – stainless steel/ aluminium.
- Flat-pack furniture – MDF.
- Flyer/leaflet – bleed-proof paper.
- Gears – low carbon steel.
- Textile sportswear – polyester/polycotton.
- Electric socket – urea formaldehyde.

15.2 1 mark each for stating two properties or characteristics of the materials that make them suitable for the selected product/ component, with a second mark each for a reason why the property makes it suitable, for example:
- Metal cooking pan – thermal conductivity **[1]** to transfer heat from the cooker to the contents of the pan **[1]**; corrosion resistance **[1]** so that the contents do not damage the pan **[1]** (or alternatively do not taint or affect the flavour of the food **[1]**); easy to form **[1]** so minimises manufacturing costs **[1]**.
- Flat-pack furniture – low cost **[1]** so makes the product more accessible to the market **[1]**; environmentally friendly **[1]** as it uses more parts of trees than planks of wood **[1]**; can be manufactured in a variety of finishes **[1]** to increase appeal to different potential customers **[1]**.
- Flyer/leaflet – low absorbency **[1]** so ink does not bleed, maintaining a sharp image **[1]**; environmentally friendly **[1]** as it can be recycled **[1]**.
- Gears – hard **[1]** so they don't wear due to the contact between gears; tough **[1]** so that gears do not break when impact between gear teeth occurs **[1]**.
- Textile sportswear – low absorbency **[1]** so it doesn't get soaked in sweat **[1]**; light weight **[1]** so that it doesn't slow down the sportsperson **[1]**.
- Electric socket – low electrical conductivity **[1]** to prevent electric shock **[1]**; tough **[1]** so it doesn't break from small impacts **[1]**.

Answers

15.3 1 mark each for stating up to four processes used during the manufacturing of the product/component. For example, this could include, where applicable, processes used for:

- Marking out.
- Wastage, such as a cutting out the material.
- Addition, such as joining parts together.
- Making the shape required, including deforming and reforming processes.

More than one process type of each type can be awarded marks, if applicable. A mark can also be given for stating the form of material used, if applicable. For example, for a metal cooking pan: cutting a blank **[1]**, pressing to form the shape **[1]** and folding over the rim **[1]**, welding on the handles **[1]**.

16.1 Up to 2 marks for detail such as: manufacture of a bespoke single item **[1]** typically by highly skilled workers **[1]**; flexible machines that may be manually controlled **[1]**.

16.2 Up to 2 marks for detail such as: fixed quantity of identical products manufactured **[1]**; jigs and templates often used to aid production **[1]**; flexible machines that can be changed over to produce different products **[1]**.

16.3 Up to 2 marks for detail such as: very large number of products produced **[1]** often using a production line **[1]**. This can involve high use of CAM (computer aided manufacture) equipment **[1]** and sub-assemblies **[1]**.

17.1 Award up to 3 marks for identifying an appropriate quality control system and details about its implementation. For example:

- Monthly magazine – use of registration marks **[1]**. These are printed outside the trim area of printing **[1]** and allow the printer to accurately align separate press plates for multi-colour print jobs **[1]**.
- Wooden wheel – go/no-go gauge **[1]**. If the wheel fits between the maximum indicators, it is less than the maximum tolerance **[1]**; if it does not fit between the markers for the minimum size, it is above the minimum tolerance **[1]**.

- Slotted metal block – using a depth stop **[1]** pre-set to the required depth **[1]** with machining stopping when the depth-stop contacts the material **[1]**.
- Polymer template – selecting the correct laser settings **[1]**, such as % power **[1]** and cutting speed **[1]**.
- Curtains – using an original sample/ master **[1]** to check the dimensions of the repeat print **[1]** and its colour **[1]**.
- PCB – controlling times for UV exposure **[1]**, developing **[1]** and etching **[1]**.

17.2 43 mm **[1]** and 47 mm **[1]**

18. 9–10 marks – excellent understanding shown and points well evaluated in depth. Appropriate and fully justified conclusions presented.

7–8 marks – good understanding shown and points well evaluated. Appropriate conclusions presented with some justification.

5–6 marks – good understanding shown with some points evaluated. Appropriate but unjustified conclusions presented.

3–4 marks – some understanding shown. Limited evaluation. Limited conclusions made.

1–2 marks – few points made or one point made with some limited explanation. No conclusion.

0 marks – no response worthy of merit.

Indicative content

Use the following as points for further evaluation to demonstrate your understanding. If you present other valid responses, you will also be given full credit. There is no requirement to use the given examples.

- Effects of sourcing different types of materials and how this affects design choices. This may include the effects of deforestation, mining, drilling and farming on both local ecology and the environment in general.
- Causes of product mileage, such as sourcing of raw materials, transportation, distribution to user and final disposal; methods of reducing product mileage

and implications for product design; environmental effects of product mileage.

- Carbon production resulting from manufacturing and its effect on the environment, such as global warming; implications of alternative production methods.
- The 6 Rs (reduce, refuse, reuse, repair, recycle and rethink) and how these affect the ecological impact of products.

Whilst candidates can answer in general terms, responses may include specific examples of products – credit will be awarded if these are appropriate.

SECTION C – Designing and Making Principles

19.1 1 mark for each relevant point of explanation, up to maximum of 2 marks per specification point chosen. For example:
- Simple function – fewer unnecessary features [1], making it easier for someone not confident with technology to use the phone [1].
- Large buttons – easier for elderly people to see the buttons/numbers [1] so suitable for users with poor eyesight [1]; easier to press [1] so suitable for people with arthritis, etc. [1].

19.2 1 mark for identifying a relevant improvement and up to 2 marks for point explaining how it would make the phone more suitable. For example:
- The phone could be given a more ergonomic shape [1]. This would make it easier to grip [1] and therefore reduce fatigue during use [1].

19.3 1 mark for each suitable point relating to colour, shape, screen size/type, features of the phone, etc. up to a maximum of 4 marks. For example:
- Including additional features on the phone such as multiple cameras [1] and WiFi access [1].
- Increasing the memory [1] so that it can hold more apps [1].
- Making it a brighter colour [1] so that it is more attractive to teenage buyers [1].
- Including a larger screen [1] so that they can see more detail when running apps or looking at social media [1].

- Having touch-sensitive capability [1] to allow data input or selection of options [1].

20.1 1 mark for making the battery life the x axis and the total number of failed batteries the y axis; 1 mark for appropriate range of values for the axes; 1 mark for a line starting at 50,0; 1 mark for points plotted at the top end of each band (70, 90, 110, 130, 150); 1 mark for a line approximating to the correct shape.

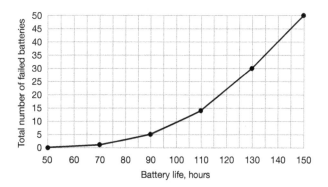

20.2 Average value = ((1 × 60) + (4 × 80) + (9 × 100) + (16 × 120) + (20 × 140))/50 [1]
= 120 hours [1]

20.3 50% of the batteries = 25 batteries [1]
Reading from the graph, this equates to a battery life of 124 hours [1].

20.4 The relationship is exponential [1], so the halfway point on the graph (50% of components) is lower than the average [1].

21.1 1 mark for each advantage given and 1 mark for further explanation of each. For example:
- Starts with a top-down overview of the system [1] so potential problems with the design can be spotted more easily/earlier in the design process [1].
- Systems diagrams do not require much technical understanding [1], so can be presented to potential users/clients who do not have a technical background [1].
- The designer can focus on producing initial ideas without worrying about the exact components needed [1], which enables greater creativity [1].
- Easier to fault-find the finished design [1] as problems can be traced back to the relevant sub-system block [1].

21.2 1 mark for each relevant point up to maximum of 4 marks, such as: it is a cyclic process [1] where a model is produced [1], the model is tested/evaluated **[1]** and then refined **[1]** leading to a new iteration **[1]**.

21.3 User-centred design **[1]**, design collaboration **[1]**.

21.4 1 mark for each suitable point up to maximum of 3 marks. For example:
- Not being able to move past the first idea **[1]**, not exploring the full range of options **[1]**, leading to potentially good design solutions being missed **[1]**.

22.1 1 mark for correct working and 1 mark for correct answer:

A = O/(tan θ)

A = 155/(tan 30˚) **[1]**

A = 268.5 mm **[1]**

22.2 1 mark for each suitable point up to maximum of 2 marks. For example:
- To provide a reference point **[1]** from which measurements can then be taken **[1]**.

22.3 1 mark for each valid method up to maximum of 2 marks, such as: nesting **[1]**, use of jigs/patterns/templates, etc. **[1]**.

23.1 1 mark for each valid reason up to maximum of 2 marks, such as: for visual/aesthetic reasons **[1]**, to protect against corrosion/oxidation/wear/damage, etc. **[1]**.

23.2 1 mark for each valid response up to maximum of 2 marks. For example:
- Papers and boards – printing **[1]**, embossing **[1]**, UV varnishing **[1]**.
- Timbers – painting **[1]**, varnishing **[1]**, tanalising **[1]**, painting **[1]**, waxing **[1]**.
- Metals – dip coating **[1]**, powder coating **[1]**, galvanising **[1]**, painting **[1]**.
- Polymers – polishing **[1]**, printing **[1]**, application of vinyl decals **[1]**.
- Textiles – printing **[1]**, applying dyes and stain protection **[1]**.
- Systems – PCB lacquering **[1]**, lubrication **[1]**.

23.3 1 mark for each point describing or showing the application of the surface treatment or finish, up to maximum of 5 marks. For example:
- Varnishing timber – sand wood to create a smooth surface **[1]**, apply filler to any holes **[1]**, use a brush to apply wood sealer or primer **[1]**, apply the varnish **[1]**, add additional coats as necessary **[1]**, allow sufficient time for each coat to dry **[1]**.
- Galvanising steel – clean the steel **[1]**, place in a molten zinc bath **[1]** of around 460° **[1]**, hold until the steel reaches the desired temperature **[1]** and the bond between the steel and zinc is formed **[1]**, quench the steel **[1]**.
- Applying vinyl decals to polymer – use a craft knife/vinyl cutter to cut the decals **[1]** from the vinyl sheet **[1]**, peel off the decals from the paper backing **[1]**, position accurately on the plastic surface **[1]**, ensure pressed smoothly onto the plastic surface **[1]**.

PRACTICE EXAM 2

SECTION A – Core Technical Principles

1.	D	**[1]**
2.	A	**[1]**
3.	A	**[1]**
4.	B	**[1]**
5.	D	**[1]**
6.	B	**[1]**
7.	B	**[1]**
8.	D	**[1]**
9.	C	**[1]**
10.	C	**[1]**

11.1
- The nuclear pile generates heat/turns water into steam **[1]**.
- The steam turns a generator, producing electricity **[1]**.

11.2 Kinetic pumped storage systems **[1]**, alkaline/rechargeable batteries **[1]**.

12.1 1 mark for naming a smart material, for example: shape memory alloys, thermochromic pigments, photochromic pigments

12.2 1 mark for stating the smart property of the material named in 12.1, for example: returns to original shape when heated, changes colour with temperature, changes colour with changes in the level of light, respectively.

13. 1 mark each for two suitable reasons, such as:
- Corrosion resistance.
- Non-toxic/will not taint food.
- Can be reused.
- Strength/doesn't bend when used.
- Can be placed in a dishwasher.
- Any other appropriate answer.

14 Mechanical advantage = load/effort
Mechanical advantage = 90/30 **[1]**
Mechanical advantage = 3 **[1]**
Note: no units as it is a ratio.

SECTION B – Specialist Technical Principles

15.1 1 mark for identifying the property modified, 1 mark for stating how it could be modified and up to 2 marks for detail about the modification or reasons why it is modified. For example:

- Polymer chair – improved durability **[1]** by adding stabilisers to resist UV degradation **[1]** as this stops sunshine weakening the polymer **[1]** as it is used outside **[1]**.
- Mass produced PCB – minimising cost **[1]** by the use of photosensitive board **[1]** to enable rapid production **[1]** of complex designs **[1]**.
- Card-based food packaging – reduced absorbency **[1]** by the use of additives to prevent moisture transfer **[1]** so that the packaging does not become soggy **[1]** when it contains hot food **[1]** that gives off moisture **[1]**.
- Metal saw blade – heat treatment **[1]** to prevent brittleness of the blade **[1]** whilst keeping a hard cutting edge **[1]**, enabling a lower cost material to be used **[1]**.
- Textile furniture covers – low flammability **[1]** by treatment with flame retardants **[1]** as this reduces risks from home fires **[1]** if it is accidentally set alight by a cigarette or electrical spark **[1]**.
- Wooden children's toy – improved dimensional stability **[1]** by seasoning **[1]** to reduce the moisture content **[1]** in case the wood is stored outside in the rain **[1]**.

Note: the use of different surface finishes with appropriate detail and reasons will also be awarded marks.

15.2 1 mark each for stating two of the 6 Rs and 1 mark each for explaining how the chosen product could be modified and the implications of this modification. For example:

- Reuse **[1]** – such as giving the wooden toy to a different child when the initial child grows older and loses interest in it **[1]**.
- Recycle **[1]** – such as melting down old saw blades so that they can be used in new products **[1]**.
- Rethink **[1]** – such as creating multi-use packaging rather than disposable food packaging **[1]**.
- Reduce **[1]** – such as making textile furniture covers that only cover the visible parts of the furniture (i.e. not the back).
- Refuse **[1]** – such as buying chairs made from sustainable material rather than polymers **[1]**.
- Repair **[1]** – such as using standard parts on the PCB to allow replacements when it fails **[1]**.

16. 1 mark for each step in the process of conversion, from sourcing to the stated form, up to a maximum of 4 marks. For example:

- Cartridge paper – cutting down trees **[1]**, pulping to form cellulose fibres **[1]**, bleaching **[1]**, spraying onto mesh screens **[1]**, etc.
- Spruce moulding – cutting down trees **[1]**, cutting planks **[1]**, seasoning **[1]**, routing/spindle moulding **[1]**.
- Zinc sheet – extraction of ore **[1]**, refining **[1]**, casting **[1]**, rolling **[1]**.
- Polyvinyl chloride rod – drilling for oil **[1]**, refining crude oil/fractional distillation **[1]**, polymerisation **[1]**, extrusion **[1]**.
- Elastane fabric – drilling for oil **[1]**, cracking the oil into its constituent parts **[1]**, polymerisation **[1]**, spinning **[1]**, etc.

17.1 1 mark for each step in the commercial manufacturing route or detail about the step, up to a maximum of 4 marks. For example:

- Pop-up book – production of lithography plates **[1]**, offset lithography **[1]**, die cutting **[1]**, adhesive bonding together **[1]**.
- Metal cylinder block – making mould **[1]**, casting **[1]**, dressing **[1]**, milling **[1]**.

- Polymer toy – making mould [1], melting plastic granules [1], injection moulding [1], cutting off of runners/sprues [1].
- Wood baseball bat – seasoning [1], turning [1], sanding [1], finishing (sealing/varnishing) [1].
- Circuits in a mobile phone – circuit board manufacture by chemical etching [1], pick and place assembly [1], flow soldering [1], testing [1].
- Curtains – weaving [1], dying [1], cutting [1], sewing [1].

17.2 1 mark each for stating two considerations and a second mark each for the reason this is a consideration, to a maximum of 4 marks. For example:
- Functionality [1] to ensure ease of use by the customer [1].
- Surface finish/texture/colour [1] to make it aesthetically appealing to the customer [1].
- Potential for recycling/reuse [1] to reduce environmental impact [1].
- Ease of sourcing/availability/opportunities for bulk buying [1] to ensure consistent supply/minimum cost [1].

18. 9–10 marks – excellent understanding shown and points well evaluated in depth. Appropriate and fully justified conclusions presented.
7–8 marks – good understanding shown and points well evaluated. Appropriate conclusions presented with some justification.
5–6 marks – good understanding shown with some points evaluated. Appropriate but unjustified conclusions presented.
3–4 marks – some understanding shown. Limited evaluation. Limited conclusions made.
1–2 marks – few points made or one point made with some limited explanation. No conclusion.
0 marks – no response worthy of merit.

Indicative content
Use the following as points for further evaluation to demonstrate your understanding. If you present other valid responses, you will also be given full credit. There is no requirement to use the given examples.

- Working conditions – conformance of factories to safety legislation and standards; legal and ethical implications of non-compliance; how conformance may vary between countries; effect on the manufacturing cost.
- Pollution – impact on marine/local habitats; potential for contamination of the food chain; potential options for reducing pollution and how these may affect the design and manufacture of products; disposal of products at the end of their life.
- Impacts on others – potential negative impacts; consideration of social footprint, ethical issues and the materials used in products; influence on the wider society.

Whilst candidates can answer in general terms, responses may include specific examples of products – credit will be awarded if these are appropriate.

SECTION C – Designing and Making Principles

19.1 3–4 marks – detailed evaluation showing clear understanding of the ergonomics of the chosen chair.
1–2 marks – mainly descriptive response showing limited understanding of the ergonomics of the chosen chair.

Indicative content
- Card side chair – seat/backrest could be curved/shaped to fit human body, straight back for posture, no arm rests, not adjustable.
- Metal garden chair – curved seat/backrest, shaped arm rest, not adjustable.
- Polymer garden chair – curved seat/backrest, shaped arm rest, not adjustable.
- Wood dining chair – seat/backrest could be curved/shaped to fit human body, straight back for posture, no arm rests, not adjustable.
- Bean bag reading chair – can be easily adjusted/shaped to whatever seating position as required, not very rigid so harder to maintain a good seating position, no arm rests.

19.2 1 mark for each past or present designer named up to maximum of 2 marks. Names of design companies will not be accepted unless a specific designer is named. Designers could include any of the following:

- Harry Beck
- Marcel Breuer
- Coco Chanel
- Norman Foster
- Alec Issigonis
- William Morris
- Alexander McQueen
- Mary Quant
- Louis Comfort Tiffany
- Raymond Templer
- Gerrit Rietveld
- Charles Rennie Macintosh
- Aldo Rossi
- Ettore Sottsass
- Philippe Starck
- Vivienne Westwood

19.3 5–6 marks – several features shown that are relevant to the style of the designer, detailed notes explaining each feature, high quality sketching.

3–4 marks – some features shown that are relevant to the style of the designer, some explanation, good quality sketching.

1–2 marks – one or two features shown that are relevant to the style of the designer, limited explanation, basic sketching.

20.1 1 mark for each advantage up to a maximum of 2 marks and 1 mark for explanation of each up to a maximum of 2 marks. For example:

- The finished product is more likely to meet user expectations [1] because their needs are considered at all stages [1].
- Users have more ownership of the final product [1] meaning they will be more likely to buy it [1].

20.2 1 mark for each disadvantage up to a maximum of 2 marks. For example:

- Takes longer to design the products [1].
- Increased expense of implementing suggested changes [1].
- Can result in products that are only suited to certain users [1].

20.3 1 mark for each suitable point up to a maximum of 2 marks, such as: it presents a top-down overview of systems [1] by splitting them into input, process and output blocks [1], uses block/systems diagrams to communicate ideas [1].

21.1 1 mark for calculating the area of the rectangle, up to 2 marks for calculating the area of the triangle and 1 mark for adding them together to give the total area.

Area of rectangle = 450 × 480

= 216 000 mm^2 [1]

Area of triangle = ½ (450 × (730 − 480)) [1]

Area of triangle = ½ × (450 × 250)

= 56 250 mm^2 [1]

Total area = 216 000 + 56 250

= 272 250 mm^2 [1]

21.2 1 mark for calculating 15% of 272 250, 1 mark for the subtraction and 1 mark for giving the answer in standard form. Alternative methods will also be accepted. Error carried forward from 21.1 will also be allowed.

0.15 × 272 250 = 40 837.5 mm^2 [1]

272 250 − 40 837.5 = 231 412.5 mm^2 [1]

= 2.31 × 10^5 mm^2 in standard form [1]

21.3 1 mark for maximum and 1 mark for the minimum permissible width.

Maximum = 452 mm **[1]**

Minimum = 448 mm **[1]**

22. 5–6 marks – detailed explanation showing a high level of understanding of how jigs, patterns or templates can be used to ensure accuracy, including a relevant and fully explained example.

3–4 marks – explanation in some detail showing a good level of understanding of how jigs, patterns or templates can be used to ensure accuracy, including a relevant example.

1–2 marks – mainly descriptive response showing a basic level of understanding of how jigs, patterns or templates can be used to ensure accuracy. An example may not be presented or may not be relevant.

Indicative content

- Holds/supports/locates the workpiece.
- Guides the cutting tool.
- Reduces the need for marking out.
- Ensures all parts are made exactly the same.
- Examples could include drill jigs, PCB holder jigs, pocket screws and/or dowelling jigs.

23.1 1 mark for correct working, 1 mark for correct answer.

Mean average = (880 + 872 + 898 + 820 + 845 + 810 + 880 + 885 + 876 + 855)/10 [1]

Mean average = 862.1 seconds [1]

23.2 1 mark converting seconds to hours, 1 mark for calculating the labour cost.

862.1 seconds = 14.37 minutes

= 0.24 hours [1]

Cost = 0.24 × 15 = £3.59 [1]

Error carried forward from 23.1 will also be allowed.

23.3 1 mark for each suitable point up to a maximum of 3 marks, such as: to test how the product/system would work [1], to show to users/clients [1] so they can suggest improvements [1], to see how the product would look in 3D [1], to spot errors in the design [1] so they can be corrected before manufacture of the final product/system begins [1], etc.

24.1 1 mark for each suitable point, such as: a set of targets [1] that a product/design/system must meet [1].

24.2 1 mark for each relevant item of information given up to a maximum of 3 marks and 1 mark for description of each up to a maximum of 3 marks. For example:

- Formal drawing of the product [1], such as orthographic [1].
- Standard components to be used [1], such as electronic circuit kits [1].
- Scale of production of the product [1], for example batch/mass/continuous production [1].
- Quality control procedures to be used [1] to ensure the product meets the defined quality criteria [1].
- Assembly instructions [1] showing how all the parts will fit together [1].